Disney · PIXAR

colour fun

Parragon

Bath • New York • Cologne • Melbourne • Delhi
Hong Kong • Shenzhen • Singapore • Amsterdam

Nemo is excited about his first day at school. But his dad, Marlin, is worried that the ocean is too dangerous.

Nemo's classmates dare him to swim into open water and touch a boat. But oh no! Nemo is kidnapped by a scuba diver.

Marlin must search the whole ocean to find his son. A blue tang named Dory agrees to help, but she is very forgetful.

Luckily, Marlin and Dory find the diver's mask
with his address. Nemo is in Sydney!

Nemo has been put in a tropical fish tank. His new friend Gill tells him he is going to be someone's pet.

Meanwhile, Marlin and Dory escape sharks, battle an anglerfish and hang out with some cool turtles on their way to rescue Nemo.

Eventually they arrive in Sydney. Gill's friend Nigel,
a pelican, carries Dory and Marlin the rest of the way.

Marlin is delighted to be reunited with his son. They have both made some new friends on their adventure!

Sulley and Mike are best friends, who work at Monsters, Inc. They collect screams from children to power Monstropolis.

One day, a little girl named Boo escapes into Monstropolis and the two friends must get her back to her world.

Mike and Sulley dress her up as a monster and sneak Boo into work. They hope to get her home without being noticed.

But a jealous co-worker called Randall wants Boo for himself
so he can steal her screams and become top scarer.

Mr Waternoose, the boss, is mad when he finds out Sulley and Mike have brought a kid into Monstropolis.

Sulley and Mike manage to rescue Boo from Randall.
They find out Waternoose is behind the whole thing.

Boo is back at home safe and sound. Sulley is sad to say goodbye.

Back at university, Mike and Sulley were very different. Mike was hardworking and eager to be the best by studying.

Sulley was laid-back and didn't care about school. He thought by being big and scary he didn't need to work hard at all.

The two monsters were always getting each other into trouble. The dean of the scaring school kicked them off the scaring programme.

The only way to get back into the school was to join a fraternity and win the scare games. Mike and Sulley join the Oozma Kappas.

Dean Hardscrabble tells Sulley that Mike is not scary and that Oozma Kappa will not win. Sulley is sad about his new friend.

But, somehow, Mike manages to win the last round of the scare games. The Oozma Kappas are the winners!

Mike is furious to find out that Sulley rigged the games so they could win. He has to prove himself so he breaks into the human world.

But Mike realizes he is not scary and will never achieve his dream of being a scarer at Monsters, Inc. Sulley comes to bring him home.

The two friends work together to scare the humans, which creates enough screams to get them home.

Dean Hardscrabble kicks them out of Monsters University but Mike and Sulley end up getting jobs at Monsters, Inc. They make a great team!

Lightning McQueen dreams of being a champion race car.

But on his way to his big race Lightning crashes in the sleepy town of Radiator Springs.

Lightning is sentenced to fix the town's road. He thinks he is too good for this and only cares about winning his race.

But Lightning begins to make friends in Radiator Springs. They teach him that some things are more important than racing.

When Lightning leaves for his race he is very sad to say goodbye to his friends – but then they all turn up at the track!

Even though he doesn't win the race, Lightning is glad to be back in Radiator Springs with all his friends.